# How To ~~Pass~~ BLITZ!
# ABRSM Theory
## Grade 4

by Samantha Coates

**Chester Music**
part of The Music Sales Group
London / New York / Paris / Sydney / Copenhagen /
Berlin / Madrid / Hong Kong / Tokyo

Published by
Chester Music,
part of The Music Sales Group,
14-15 Berners Street,
London W1T 3LJ, UK.

Exclusive Distributors:
Music Sales Limited
Distribution Centre, Newmarket Road,
Bury St Edmunds, Suffolk IP33 3YB, UK.

Music Sales Pty Limited
4th floor, Lisgar House,
30-32 Carrington Street,
Sydney, NSW 2000, Australia.

Order No. CH85657
ISBN 978-1-78558-490-9

Printed in the EU.

Your Guarantee of Quality:

As publishers, we strive to produce every book
to the highest commercial standards.

Particular care has been given to specifying acid-free, neutral-sized
paper made from pulps which have not been elemental chlorine bleached.

This pulp is from farmed sustainable forests and was
produced with special regard for the environment.

Throughout, the printing and binding have been planned to ensure
a sturdy, attractive publication which should give years of enjoyment.

If your copy fails to meet our high standards,
please inform us and we will gladly replace it.

www.musicsales.com

# A Note From the Author

Dear theory student,

Congratulations! You have just done the very best thing for your theory education — you've bought this book.

This Grade 4 theory workbook contains more information, more revision and more worksheets than any other theory text book (except maybe How To Blitz! ABRSM Theory Grades 1–3!).

There are LOTS of new things to learn in Grade 4, but what you need to know is that this book builds on the knowledge you gained in Grades 1–3. If you are 'jumping in' at Grade 4 level, there may be some things you need to brush up on. All of this is outlined on page 5, but the best strategy is to work through the workbooks from previous grades before you start this book. Discuss this more with your teacher, of course.

Every time you see this icon:  it means there are extra resources available on the website.

Go to www.blitzbooks.com to download free worksheets, flashcards, manuscript and more!

Happy theory-ing,

Samantha

It takes more than an author and a publisher to produce a book — it takes enormous support from friends and family. Thank you to everyone who has helped me on the BlitzBooks journey, but most of all to Andrew, Thomas and Courtney... without you three, there would simply be no books.

# Contents

# Things You Should Know

If you are jumping in at Grade 4 level, you'll notice there is a lot of assumed knowledge from previous grades. The very best way for you to get up to speed is to go through the How to Blitz! ABRSM Theory workbooks for Grades 1, 2 and 3!

Let's do a very quick overview of the concepts that were covered in Grades 1-3. You'll need to brush up on all of this with your teacher.

## KEY SIGNATURES

Major and minor keys with up to four sharps or flats, and the major and minor scales of these keys.

## TIME SIGNATURES

Simple: $\frac{2}{4}$, $\frac{3}{4}$, $\frac{4}{4}$, $\mathbf{C}$, $\frac{3}{8}$, $\frac{2}{2}$, $\frac{3}{2}$ and $\frac{4}{2}$

Compound: $\frac{6}{8}$, $\frac{9}{8}$, $\frac{12}{8}$

## NOTE VALUES

All note and rest values from semibreve down to demisemiquaver, and the correct groupings of notes and rests within time signatures, including the use of triplets.

## OTHER STUFF

To prepare for Grade 4, you should know how to go about any of the following tasks, because these could easily crop up in your exam:

★ Rewrite melodies in different clefs, at the same pitch or up/down an octave

★ Fix beaming and grouping errors

★ Compose a four-bar rhythm in any of the above time signatures

★ Rewrite melodies with notes of half or twice the value

★ Mark the phrasing in melodies

★ Translate the Italian terms you learned in Grades 1-3!

Got all that? Then you're ready to tackle Grade 4! Turn the page!

# Double Sharps and Double Flats

A double sharp sign looks like this: ✗ . It **raises** a note by two semitones (one tone).

A double flat sign looks like this: ♭♭. It **lowers** a note by two semitones (one tone).

Raise all of these notes one tone with a double sharp (written as '✗'):

Lower all of these notes one tone with a double flat:

Now play all these notes on your instrument! (Well, as many as you can anyway)

Double sharps and double flats enable us to write the same note three different ways.

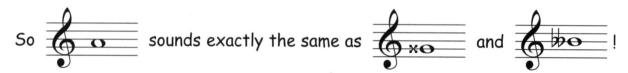

Notes with different letter names but the same sound are called **enharmonic equivalents**. Write TWO enharmonic equivalents for each of these notes. Be careful: sometimes you may only need a single sharp or flat!

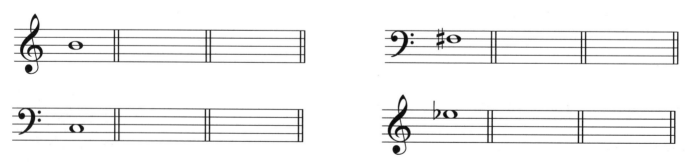

Rewrite this melody, keeping the pitch the same but without using any accidentals at all.

Do you recognise the tune???

# New Sharp Keys

In Grades 1–3 we learned about keys with up to four sharps:

G major/E minor    D major/B minor    A major/F# minor    E major/C# minor

Well guess what? There is only one new key signature for Grade 4! It's for the keys of B major and G# minor, and it has... you guessed it... FIVE sharps:

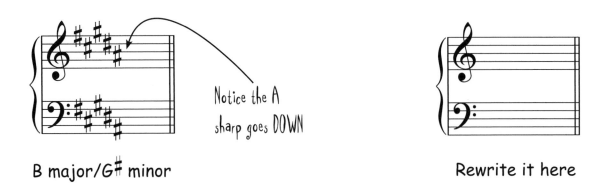

Notice the A sharp goes DOWN

B major/G# minor                                    Rewrite it here

Write the following key signatures and tonic triads (watch out for clef changes!):

F# minor            B major            C# minor            B major

Write a B major scale:

★  use treble clef and write in semibreves

★  use accidentals, not a key signature

★  write one octave ascending

# Double Sharps in Scales

In harmonic minor scales we always have to raise the leading note. Up until now we've used a sharp or a natural sign to do this, but what if the leading note is already a sharp???

Let's look at a harmonic minor scale in one of our new keys, G♯ harmonic minor:

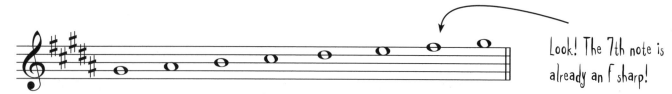

Look! The 7th note is already an f sharp!

We can't just use a sharp to raise the 7th note, we need a **double sharp**! (Add this now)

**P.S.** Adding a double sharp overrides the key signature. It does not make it a triple sharp!

What about G♯ melodic minor? It's a little more complicated:

Double sharp needed here!

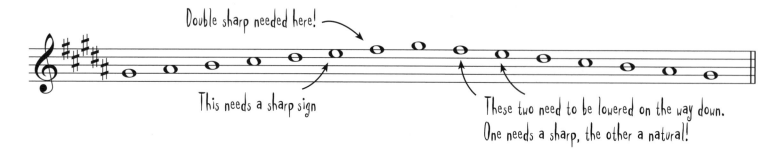

This needs a sharp sign

These two need to be lowered on the way down. One needs a sharp, the other a natural!

**P.S.** A single sharp sign is enough to cancel out a double sharp sign.

Write the scale of G♯ harmonic minor:

★ use a key signature

★ use semibreves

★ write one octave going down and then back up again (did you read that carefully?)

IMPORTANT: Even though f double sharp is the same as a G, you may NOT write a G as the 7th note in your scale – this would make two Gs, which is not allowed in a 'diatonic' scale. In diatonic scales each note must have a different letter name!

# New Flat Keys

D♭ major and B♭ minor are new in Grade 4. Now you know all the keys with up to five flats!

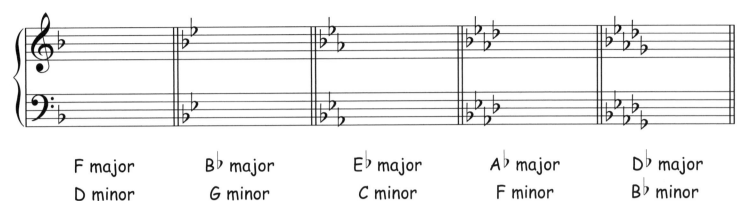

| F major | B♭ major | E♭ major | A♭ major | D♭ major |
| D minor | G minor | C minor | F minor | B♭ minor |

Write these key signatures and tonic triads (watch out for clef changes!):

| F minor | A♭ major | D♭ major | B♭ minor | C minor |

DID YOU KNOW... The Blitz Key Signature Table is the perfect aid for memorising key signatures!

Write the major scale with the key signature of five flats:

★ use accidentals instead of a key signature

★ write in minims

★ write one octave descending

Quick Question: Is there ever a need to use a double flat in a scale?

Quick Answer: _____

# The Chromatic Scale

A chromatic scale is made up of **semitones only**. This means there are 13 different notes in a one-octave scale!

The example above is just one way to write a chromatic scale on C. Here is another, rather ridiculous way to write it:

Believe it or not, these notes are all one semitone apart! It's too hard to read music written like this, so there are rules when writing chromatic scales:

1. No more than two notes on any line or space

2. No skipping of any line or space

Let's add accidentals to make this into a chromatic scale on D:

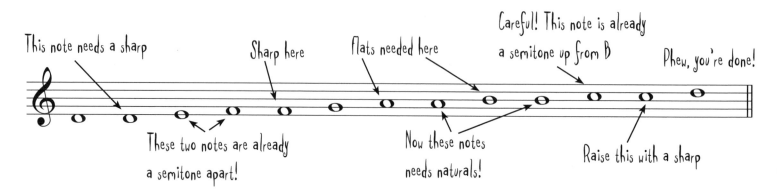

Good job! Now try it again, this time making a chromatic scale on F. But watch out... there's a key signature, so that means the B is a B♭!

Finish this chromatic scale on G:

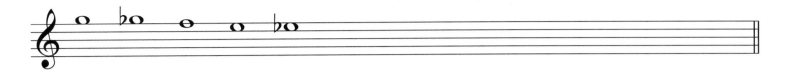

Now it's time to recognise chromatic scales in music. Put a bracket over the chromatic scale in this excerpt:

Rimsky-Korsakov

Good work! Here's some music by Chopin that features two sets of chromatic notes (not a whole scale, but part of it). There is a bracket over the first set. Can you find the other?

Chopin

Can you spot which of the following tunes are based **entirely** on chromatic scales? (Circle Yes or No) If there are any intervals larger than a semitone, it's not all chromatic!

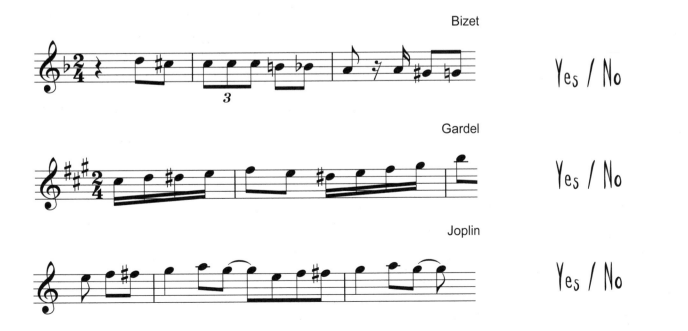

Bizet

Yes / No

Gardel

Yes / No

Joplin

Yes / No

11

# The Alto Clef

This is an alto clef: 𝄡 It looks sort of like a fancy letter B.

In alto clef, middle C is on the third line: 𝄡 ○ Wow! This is MIDDLE C!

So this 𝄡 ○ sounds exactly the same as this 𝄞 and this 𝄢 !

Here's how you draw an alto clef:

First draw two vertical lines (the first one does not have to be thick) , then draw two

little diagonal lines from the middle line . Then draw two backward 'C' shapes from

the end of each little line like this and this ... and voilà! You have an alto clef!

Trace and draw loads of alto clefs. (You can even put blobs on the end of the C shapes if you want to get really fancy!)

You may be thinking, 'why on earth do we need another clef?!' but alto clef is very useful for viola players, because of the range of their instrument (see page 56 for information on the viola). Violas tend to play a lot of notes around middle C, and it's a real pain having to read leger lines all the time. So, they read in alto clef instead.

Here is 'Twinkle, Twinkle, Little Star' written in G major, at the same pitch in three different clefs. Alto clef is the only one that doesn't use leger lines - much easier to read!

Key signatures look very different in alto clef. Check these out:

The position of key signatures in alto clef is one note lower than treble (or one note higher than bass!)

Write these key signatures in alto clef:

F# minor          A♭ major          G# minor          B♭ major          C minor

Rewrite the following notes in alto clef, keeping the pitch the same. All you need to do is keep the position of middle C (shown in grey) in your head at all times.

Rewrite these short melodies in alto clef. As long as you get the first note in the right spot, the rest is simple! Don't forget that the key signatures will move too.

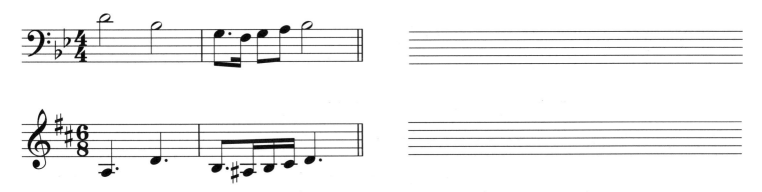

And for your final trick... rewrite this short melody at the same pitch in treble clef.

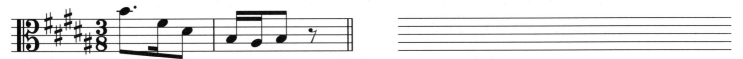

# Scale Degree Names

There have been lots of times we've referred to scale degree no. 1 as the 'tonic' (e.g. tonic triads). This is known as a **technical** scale degree name. Now it's time to learn the technical names for all the other scale degrees!

| Scale Degree | Technical Name | Handy Hint for Remembering |
|:---:|:---:|:---:|
| 1 | TONIC | you already know this one |
| 2 | SUPERTONIC | 'super' means above |
| 3 | MEDIANT | think 'Do-Re-**Me**diant'! |
| 4 | SUBDOMINANT | 'sub' means 'under': no. 4 is under no. 5! |
| 5 | DOMINANT | scale degree no. 5 tends to be '**dominant**' in the harmony |
| 6 | SUBMEDIANT | mediant is three **above** (1-2-**3**), so 'sub' mediant is three **below** (1-7-**6**) |
| 7 | LEADING NOTE | it 'leads' to the tonic! |

These notes are all from C major. Can you write the correct scale degree name under each?

And now here are some from G minor... all in alto clef! Name these:

Notice anything about the leading note in the exercises above? That's right, it is RAISED in the minor key. Burn this into your memory!

Write the following key signatures and scale degrees. Watch out for alto clef!

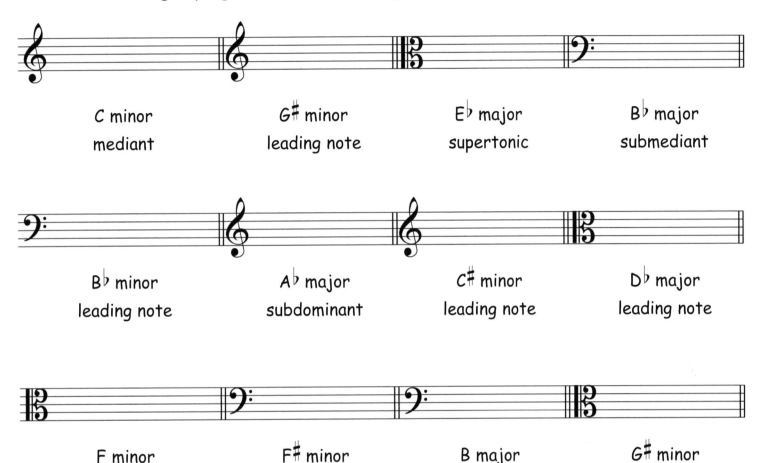

C minor
mediant

G# minor
leading note

E♭ major
supertonic

B♭ major
submediant

B♭ minor
leading note

A♭ major
subdominant

C# minor
leading note

D♭ major
leading note

F minor
supertonic

F# minor
leading note

B major
dominant

G# minor
tonic

Add accidentals to make the following leading notes correct (they are all minor keys):

Add the correct clef and key signature to make these scale degrees correct.

A♭ major, dominant

B minor, supertonic

E minor, leading note

# Tiny Test

1. Name these **major** keys and technical scale degrees (e.g. tonic, mediant etc.)   /10

Key: _____  _____  _____  _____  _____

Degree: _____  _____  _____  _____  _____

2. Write the scale of B♭ harmonic minor, using the ALTO clef. Use semibreves and write one octave descending.  /8

3. Name these notes. The first one has been done for you (yay!).   /5

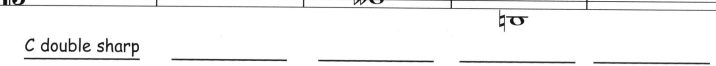

<u>C double sharp</u>  _____  _____  _____  _____

4. Follow the instructions below to make this melody correct.  /6

★ Add the correct clef

★ Complete bar two by adding a triplet sign in an appropiate place

★ Find all the leading notes and raise them. (Think!)

★ Put a bracket over five consecutive notes that form part of a chromatic scale

★ Add the correct rest/s in the final bar

5. Add a clef and key signature to make these the correct technical scale degrees. /6

C minor, leading note          B major, dominant          F# minor, supertonic

6. Write an ascending chromatic scale beginning on the given note. /10

7. Rewrite the melody from question 4 (assuming you completed it and are not doing this test completely out of order) in the treble clef, without changing the pitch. Remember to write the key signature and time signature! /10

8. Name two keys that share this key signature: /2

1._____

2._____

9. Name a minor scale that needs a double sharp: _____ /1

10. Write two different notes that are enharmonic equivalents of this note: /2

Total: /60   (This test wasn't so tiny after all)

# Breves and Double Dots

A breve looks like a semibreve with two vertical lines on either side: ‖O‖

It is equivalent to two semibreves (just like a cirle is equivalent to two semicircles!). This means it is worth EIGHT crotchet beats! (Wow) It fills up a whole bar of $\frac{4}{2}$ time.

Finish this B major scale written in breves. As you can see, accidentals are written to the left of the vertical lines:

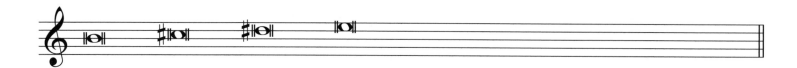

If you think the breve looks weird, wait until you see the breve rest! It's like a semibreve rest and a minim rest combined into one skinny solid block: ▬ .

$\frac{4}{2}$ is the **only** time signature where you'll find a breve or a breve rest in Grade 4 (and you don't see them much at all in general music!). It's also the only time signature in which a semibreve rest fills **half** a bar with silence. Complete these bars as directed:

| 2 notes and 1 rest | 1 note | 1 note and 1 rest | 1 rest |

Unlike breves and breve rests, **double-dotted** notes are found in music all the time.

The second dot is worth half the value of the first dot. So ♩.. = ♩ + ♪ + ♪ = $1\frac{3}{4}$!

A really great trick for working with double dots is to remember that the very next note value will be ONE QUARTER of the value of the undotted note! For example:

♪.. is followed by ♬ (because ♬ is worth $\frac{1}{4}$ of ♪)!

Complete the first bar with the correct note, and the next two bars with the correct rest.

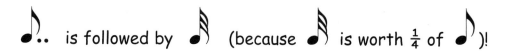

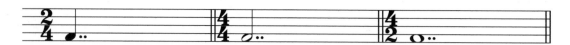

# Simple Time Signatures

According to the Grade 4 syllabus you are required to know 'all simple time signatures'. Simple time signatures have any number on the top, and any power of two on the bottom!

You may be thinking this means you have to know time signatures such as this:

This means four hemidemisemiquaver beats per bar, which is a bit ridiculous

The good news is that you only have to know simple time signatures with the bottom numbers of 2 (minim beats), 4 (crotchet beats), or 8 (quaver beats). Phew!

Fill in the table below with simple time signatures and compose an interesting bar of rhythm for each!

| | Simple Duple (2 on top) | Simple Triple (3 on top) | Simple Quadruple (4 on top) |
|---|---|---|---|
| Minim Beats (2 on Bottom) | $\frac{2}{2}$ ♩ ♫♫♪ | | |
| Crotchet Beats (4 on Bottom) | | | |
| Quaver Beats (8 on Bottom) | | | |

## THINGS TO KNOW:

★ $\frac{2}{8}$ is not very common at all, so you won't be tested on this time signature in your exam.

★ $\frac{4}{8}$ is the new simple time signature for Grade 4. It looks no different from $\frac{2}{4}$!

Add the correct time signature to these one-bar rhythms:

# Compound Time Signatures

In Grade 3 you learned about compound time signatures with a **top** number of 6, 9, or 12. The time signatures you need to know in Grade 4 have a **bottom** number of 4, 8 or 16.

We haven't had 16 as a bottom number before! This means that there are **semiquavers** grouped three at a time.

Fill in this table with the correct compound time signatures, and compose a bar for each!

| | Compound Duple (6 on top) | Compound Triple (9 on top) | Compound Quadruple (12 on top) |
|---|---|---|---|
| Dotted Minim Beats (4 on Bottom) | $\frac{6}{4}$ ♩ ♫ ♩ ♩. | | |
| Dotted Crotchet Beats (8 on Bottom) | | | |
| Dotted Quaver Beats (16 on Bottom) | | | |

**THINGS TO KNOW:**

★ The new compound time signatures for Grade 4 are $\frac{6}{4}$, $\frac{9}{4}$, $\frac{6}{16}$, $\frac{9}{16}$ and $\frac{12}{16}$. You don't come across $\frac{12}{4}$ very often in music, so you won't be tested on that.

★ The rules for grouping in the new compound time signatures are just the same as you learned in Grade 3. Remember to group notes and rests in THREES.

Add the correct time signatures to these one-bar rhythms:

20

# The Duplet

A quaver duplet looks like this ♪♪ or like this 𝄽 and is equal to three quavers, or one dotted crotchet beat. For instance:

Of course, there are other types of duplets, such as crotchet or semiquaver duplets:

The definition of a duplet is:

**'Two notes played in the time of three notes of equal value'** (learn this!)

Add time signatures and the missing bar-lines to these melodies featuring duplets.

Complete these bars with the correct rest/s:

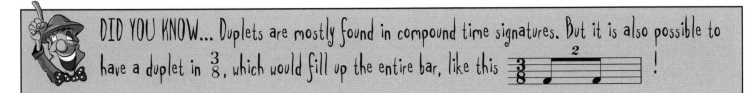

DID YOU KNOW... Duplets are mostly found in compound time signatures. But it is also possible to have a duplet in $\frac{3}{8}$, which would fill up the entire bar, like this !

21

# Add the Missing...

<--->

... time signatures to these five excerpts:

Bach

Bach

Liszt

Bach

Hughes

... time signature AND bar-lines to this **three-bar** extract:

Bach

... time signature AND bar-lines to this **five-bar** extract:

Grieg

... rest to complete each of the first four bars of this excerpt:

Bach

... bar-lines to this melody:

Dvořák

... key signature (D flat major) and time signature to this extract:

Debussy

... key signature, time signature and bar-lines to this **four-bar** melody (which is in a major key and starts on the tonic!):

Mozart

# Compound to Simple

When you hear a rhythm that sounds like it may be in compound time, there is actually a possibility it may be written in simple time, but using triplets. Clap these, and notice that:

   sounds the same as

   sounds the same as

   sounds the same as

Can you see the pattern? To convert from compound to simple time, all you need to do is:

1. Convert the time signature:   $\dfrac{\text{Top number} \div 3}{\text{Bottom number} \div 2}$   (e.g. $\frac{6}{8}$ becomes $\frac{2}{4}$ )

2. **Add** triplet signs to all groups of three

3. **Remove** duplet signs from all groups of two

4. Dotted beats become undotted beats

Using the formula above, convert these time signatures from compound to simple:

| $\frac{9}{8}$ $\longrightarrow$ | $\frac{12}{16}$ $\longrightarrow$ | $\frac{6}{4}$ $\longrightarrow$ | $\frac{9}{16}$ $\longrightarrow$ |
|---|---|---|---|

Following the steps above, convert these melodies from compound to simple.

Play these melodies or get someone to play them for you. Can you tell which time signature is being played, just by the sound???

24

# Simple to Compound

You guessed it... converting from simple to compound involves doing the exact opposite of what you did on the previous page!

1.  Convert the time signature: $\dfrac{\text{Top number} \times 3}{\text{Bottom number} \times 2}$    (e.g. $\frac{2}{4}$ becomes $\frac{6}{8}$)

2.  **Remove** triplet signs from all groups of three

3.  **Add** duplet signs to all groups of two

4.  Undotted beats become dotted beats

Using the formula above, convert these time signatures from simple to compound:

| $\frac{2}{4}$ → | $\frac{3}{8}$ → | $\frac{3}{2}$ → | $\frac{4}{4}$ → |
|---|---|---|---|

Convert these melodies from simple to compound (i.e. undotted beats to dotted beats). Find the new time signature, and remember to REMOVE triplets and ADD duplets!

 HERE'S A THOUGHT... it is impossible to know the time signature of a piece of music just by listening to it. See if you can trick someone, especially your teacher!

# Revision of Stuff So Far

1. Answer the bunch of questions below about this music:

Bach

a. It contains notes of the tonic triad in bar 3. What key is it in? _____

b. Insert the correct time signature and describe it as (circle correct answers):

   simple / compound          **and**          duple / triple / quadruple

c. Rewrite bars 2 and 3 of the left-hand (bass) part so that it sounds the same but has a simple time signature instead. Write the key signature and the new time signature.

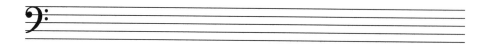

d. How many semiquavers is the tied note in bar 2 worth? ____

e. Who wrote this music? _____ (a real test of your observation skills)

2. Here is another excerpt. Place a bracket over four consecutive notes that form part of a chromatic scale.

Mozart

3. Write as a breve an enharmonic equivalent of the last note of bar 1 (of question 2).

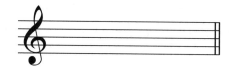

4.  The above extract from Debussy's *Clair de Lune* is in ____ major.

a.  Insert the correct time signature.

b.  Look at the circled chord in bar 6. How many demismemiquavers is this worth? ____

c.  How many bars contain duplets? ___

d.  Ignoring the ties, rewrite the top part (i.e. no chords) of bar 7 in simple time. Write the new time signature.

e.  Rewrite the last note of bar 7 in the alto clef. Do not use a key signature (which is code for 'you may need to use an accidental').

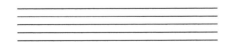

5.  All of the extracts in this revision test are in simple/compound time (circle correct answer).

# Composing Rhythms

You've composed so many four-bar rhythms in Grades 1–3 that you're an expert by now! It's time to use your fabulous creative skills in the new time signatures for Grade 4.

Remember, a **mixture** of repetition and contrast works best. You don't want your melody to sound too boring and repetitive, but you also don't want it to sound completely random and unbalanced. Revise all the hints in the Grade 3 workbook, and discuss with your teacher.

Compose four-bar rhythms based on the following openings. Sometimes you need to complete the first bar. Also, remember to adjust your final bar if there is an anacrusis.

You don't have to complete all of these at once. Doing one or two per week works really well! And the most important thing of all... CLAP your rhythms to yourself and to your teacher!

# Rewrite This

In Grade 3 you did loads of rewriting of melodies. Time for some more! You'll be rewriting this melody four times. It's a good idea to revise your halving/doubling skills, and transposing up or down an octave!

1. Rewrite this melody with notes and rests of HALF the value.

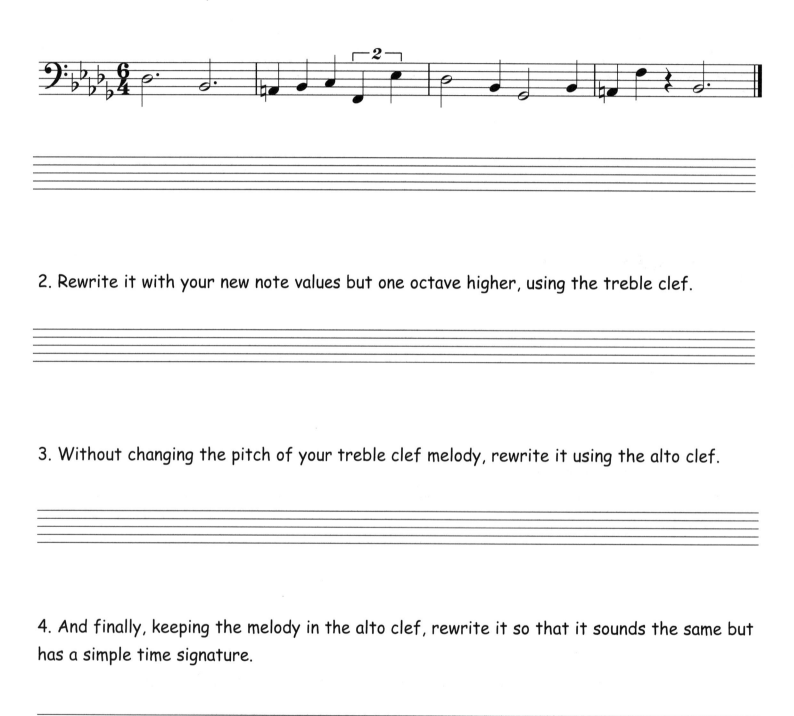

2. Rewrite it with your new note values but one octave higher, using the treble clef.

3. Without changing the pitch of your treble clef melody, rewrite it using the alto clef.

4. And finally, keeping the melody in the alto clef, rewrite it so that it sounds the same but has a simple time signature.

There, you're done! Has the sound of the melody changed? Yes / No (circle correct answer)

# Intervals

In Grade 3 you learned that intervals have a type as well as a number: they can be **major**, **minor** or **perfect**. Name the following intervals (some melodic, some harmonic), which are all in the key of E♭ major:

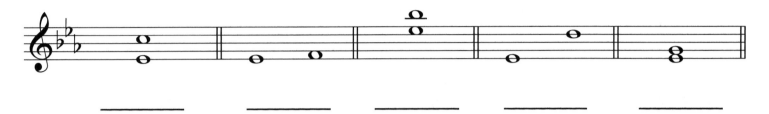

Here are some more intervals, this time in the key of G♯ minor. Remember, if the 7th note is raised, it's a major 7th, and if not, it's a minor 7th!

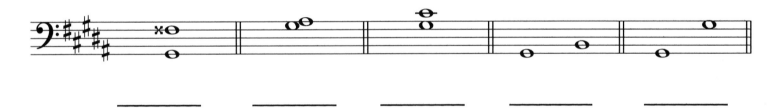

Now things get a little more tricky. In Grade 4, you are not told the key! However, all you need to do is treat the bottom note as the tonic, and you can work out the type of interval by thinking of the major or minor scales that begin on that note. Name these intervals:

Now **write** these intervals. You may use accidentals OR a key signature for each. Treat the given note as the tonic.

     perfect 5th        major 7th        minor 6th        perfect 4th        minor 3rd

# Diminished and Augmented Intervals

Up until now we've only come across major, minor or perfect intervals. But in Grade 4 we need to know about two other types of intervals:

★ **AUGMENTED (aug)** = one semitone **larger** than major or perfect.

★ **DIMINISHED (dim)** = one semitone **smaller** than minor or perfect.

To help you fill in the table below, let's think of major and minor intervals as one species, (e.g. fish) and perfect intervals as another species (e.g. spiders). As the fish or spider 'grows' it is becoming one semitone larger.

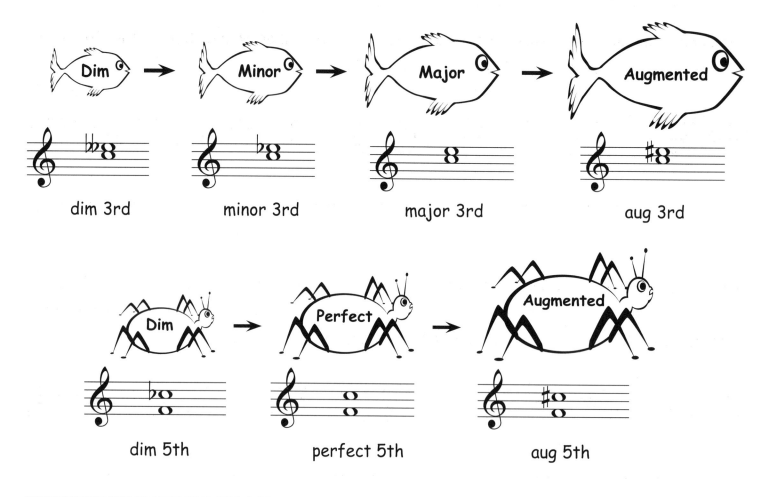

| dim 3rd | minor 3rd | major 3rd | aug 3rd |

| dim 5th | perfect 5th | aug 5th |

| Type of Interval | One Semitone Larger | One Semitone Smaller |
|---|---|---|
| Major (e.g. 2nds, 3rds, 6ths and 7ths) | | |
| Minor (e.g. 2nds, 3rds, 6ths and 7ths) | | |
| Perfect (e.g. unisons, 4ths, 5ths and 8ves) | | |

Intervals can be made larger or smaller by adding accidentals to the top **or** bottom note, or even both! For example:

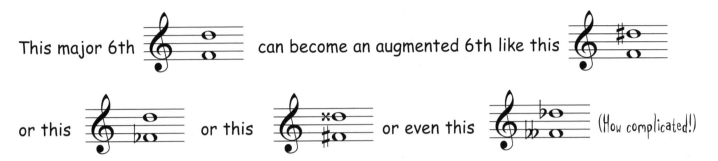

All of the following intervals are either major or perfect. Add an accidental to the **top** note to transform them into augmented or diminished intervals as indicated.

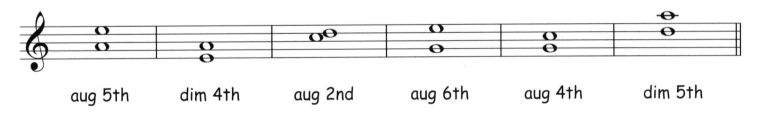

| aug 5th | dim 4th | aug 2nd | aug 6th | aug 4th | dim 5th |

All of these intervals are minor or perfect. Add an accidental to the **bottom** note to make them augmented or diminished as indicated.

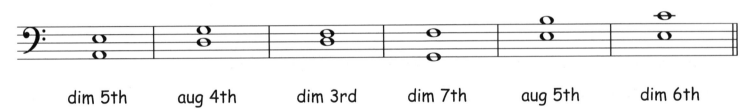

| dim 5th | aug 4th | dim 3rd | dim 7th | aug 5th | dim 6th |

In your exam you're often asked to name intervals in a melody. Always treat the lower note of the interval as the tonic – then think in that key. (You'll need to think carefully about the major AND minor scales when naming 3rds or 6ths.) Name the bracketed intervals in this Mozart melody:

33

# Naming Intervals

Grade 4 intervals are trickier than before because you may be given **any** two notes from a scale, not necessarily the tonic. This means it is hard to work within a key, especially with complicated accidentals. So the solution is... ignore the accidentals! (good stuff)

Imagine you've been asked to name this interval:

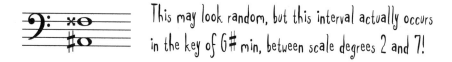

This may look random, but this interval actually occurs in the key of G# min, between scale degrees 2 and 7!

Most people go into a mild panic when they see the double sharp, let alone trying to think in the key of A#! But if you strip the accidentals away, you get the 'naked' interval...

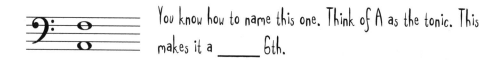

You know how to name this one. Think of A as the tonic. This makes it a _____ 6th.

Easy! Now all we have to do is 'dress' the interval again by putting the accidentals back in, and see if the distance between the notes remains the same.

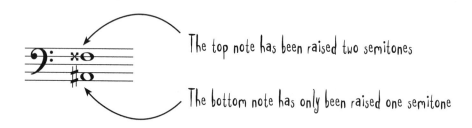

The top note has been raised two semitones

The bottom note has only been raised one semitone

So the accidentals have made this interval one semitone larger/smaller (circle correct answer).
This transforms it from a _____ 6th into a _____ 6th. (Go over the table on page 32 if you need help!)

---

**Interesting Fact I**: Intervals without accidentals are ALWAYS major, minor or perfect, except for these two:

aug 4th        and        dim 5th

**Interesting Fact II**: The quality of an interval does not change if you add the same accidental to both the top and bottom notes!

| 'Dressed' interval | Draw it without accidentals ('undress' it) | Name the 'naked' interval | Describe how the accidentals affect the interval | Now name the 'dressed' interval! |
|---|---|---|---|---|
| | | major 6th | top note is one semitone higher, bottom note is two semitones higher, therefore the interval is **one semitone smaller** | minor 6th |
| | | | | |
| | | | | |
| | | | | |
| | | | | |
| | | | | |
| | | | | |
| | | | | |
| | | | | |
| | | | | |

35

# Intervals With Key Signatures

If you are asked to name an interval from a melody with a key signature, just rewrite the interval with accidentals instead.

For instance, simply convert  into

The accidental does not change when you remove the key signature

Then name the interval by removing the accidentals first and so on – you know the drill! The name of the above interval is _____.

Here is a melody with a few intervals for you to identify, marked A, B and C. As you can see, there is a key signature at the beginning, so this will affect the notes in the intervals.

Rewrite each labelled interval on the staves below, using accidentals instead of a key signature. Then name them, using the process we drilled on page 35!

Rewrite interval A      Name: _____

Rewrite interval B      Name: _____

Rewrite interval C      Name: _____

Great work! Now name these intervals. You can try to 'imagine' them with accidentals instead of a key signature, or you can use spare manuscript to rewrite them.

# Interesting Intervals

Name the intervals indicated by the brackets and letters A-E. If you need to rewrite them on some spare manuscript, you can download some from **www.blitzbooks.com**.

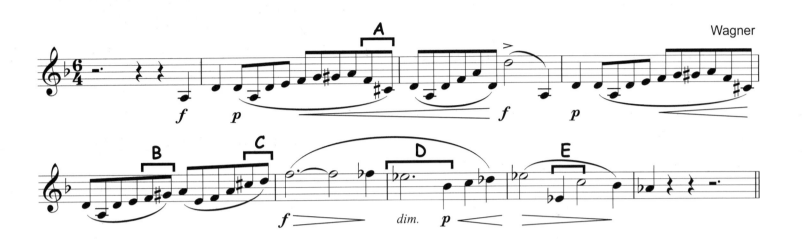

Interval A: _____     Interval D: _____

Interval B: _____     Interval E: _____

Interval C: _____

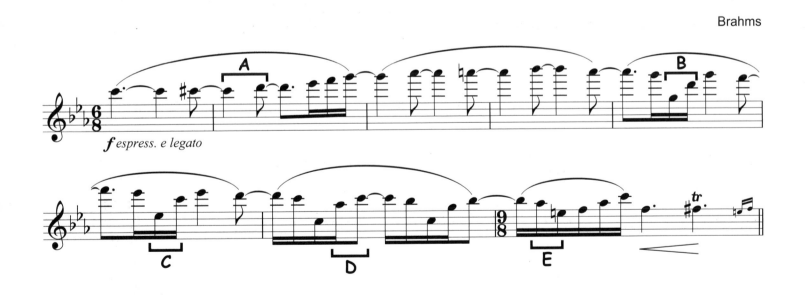

Interval A: _____     Interval D: _____

Interval B: _____     Interval E: _____

Interval C: _____

# Yet More Revision

1.  Answer the questions below about this extract.

Paganini

a.  Identify (by number and type, of course) the intervals marked with brackets.

Interval A: _____

Interval B: _____

Interval C: _____

b.  Name the scale formed by every **second** semiquaver in bar 2. _____

c.  Rewrite the first six semiquavers of the extract at the same pitch using the alto clef.

2.  Add the correct clef and key signature to this scale (there is only one possible answer):

3.  Rewrite this extract with correct beaming of notes and rests (this is revision of Grade 3 stuff!).

Scarlatti

4. A double dot after a note makes it:

 A: twice as long

 B: 1½ times as long

 C: 1¾ times as long

5. Here come a few things to do for this melody:

★ Add the correct time signature

★ True or false: the notes of bar 4 make up a D minor triad. _____

★ Write as a breve the enharmonic equivalent of the first note of bar 3.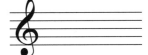

★ How many semiquavers are in the tied note in bar 2? _____

★ Rewrite bars 1–4, using notes of twice the value. Write the new time signature. (Hint: only the bottom number of the time signature changes!)

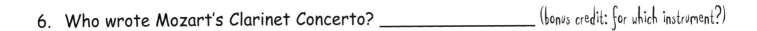

6. Who wrote Mozart's Clarinet Concerto? _____ (bonus credit: for which instrument?)

7. Compose a four-bar rhythm using this opening. Watch out for the anacrusis, and remember to complete the first bar.

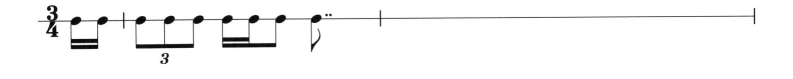

# Triads

In Grades 1-3 we worked with the **tonic** triad, also known as chord I because it is built on scale degree no. 1. If we build a triad on scale degree no. 4, it is the **subdominant** triad (chord IV), and a triad on no. 5 is – you guessed it – the **dominant** triad (chord V).

Let's look at C major triads:

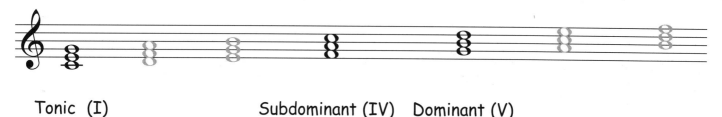

Tonic (I)                    Subdominant (IV)   Dominant (V)

The chords on the tonic (I), subdominant (IV) and dominant (V) are known as the three **PRIMARY** triads. (Notice that we always use Roman numerals when referring to chords!)

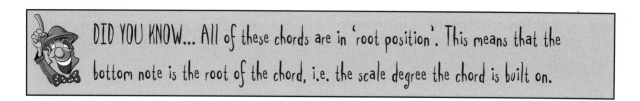

DID YOU KNOW... All of these chords are in 'root position'. This means that the bottom note is the root of the chord, i.e. the scale degree the chord is built on.

Write the three primary triads in the following **major** keys, then write the name and number of each chord underneath. (Watch out for clef changes!)

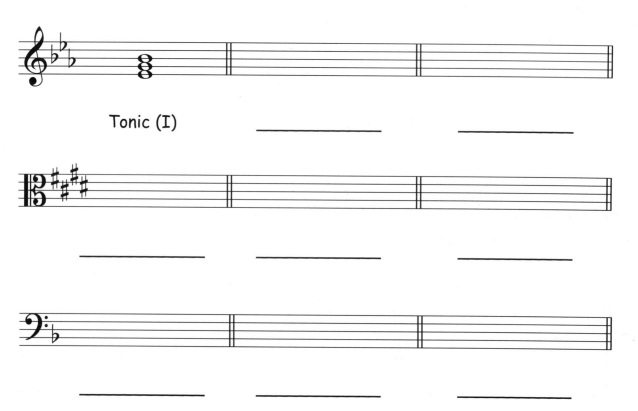

Tonic (I)              _____        _____

_____        _____        _____

_____        _____        _____

# Naming Triads

Here is a typically worded exam question:

'Identify these triads by naming the key and describing them as tonic (I), subdominant (IV) or dominant (V).'

This means that your answer **must** be either I, IV, or V.  If you end up with any other chord number as your answer it will be WRONG! (Which would be sad)

This key signature could be D major or B minor

The bottom note (the root) is B

OK, here's the REALLY IMPORTANT BIT!

In D major, the note B is scale degree no. 6, so this would be chord VI.

In B minor, the note B is scale degree no. 1, so this would be chord I.

Which answer is correct? Remember... your answer must end up as I, IV, or V...

So the answer is chord _____ in _____.

Name these key signatures and triads as I, IV or V.

Key: _____   _____   _____   _____   _____

Triad: _____   _____   _____   _____   _____

Key: _____   _____   _____   _____   _____

Triad: _____   _____   _____   _____   _____

# Chord V in Minor Keys

Chord V contains the leading note (7th note), and – as you know – in minor keys the leading note needs to be raised. Let's look at chord V in G minor and B♭ minor:

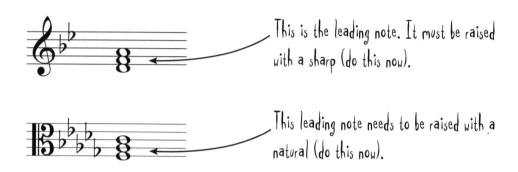

This is the leading note. It must be raised with a sharp (do this now).

This leading note needs to be raised with a natural (do this now).

DID YOU KNOW... In root position, the leading note is always the MIDDLE note of chord V!

The following are all dominant triads in minor keys. Raise the leading note (middle note) of each chord by adding the correct accidental:

Some of the dominant triads below are from **major** keys, which means you don't need to raise the leading note! Work out which of these chords are from minor keys and raise the leading note with the correct accidental.

Tricky!

Write these **dominant** triads with key signatures (remember to raise the leading note in minor keys only)!

| D♭ major | C minor | B minor | F minor | B major |
|----------|---------|---------|---------|---------|
| dominant (V) | dominant (V) | dominant (V) | dominant (V) | dominant (V) |

# Terrific Triads

1. Name the following keys, then name each triad as either the tonic (I), subdominant (IV) or dominant (V) of that key.

Key: _____     Key: _____     Key: _____

Triad: _____     Triad: _____     Triad: _____

2. When writing triads, we must take special care with: (circle correct answer)

   A.   Chord V in all keys

   B.   Chord V in minor keys only

   C.   Chords I, IV and V in minor keys

3. Write these triads in root position with key signatures.

| D major | F# minor | E major | C minor | Bb minor |
|---------|----------|---------|---------|----------|
| dominant (V) | subdominant (IV) | tonic (I) | dominant (V) | tonic (I) |

| A major | E minor | A minor | Bb major | C# minor |
|---------|---------|---------|----------|----------|
| subdominant (IV) | dominant (V) | subdominant (IV) | tonic (I) | dominant (V) |

4. Here are three tonic triads. Choose a different clef and key signature for each one. Then name the keys you've created. (N.B. There are several different ways to complete this question!)

Key: _____     Key: _____     Key: _____

# Chords

The notes of any triad can be used to form more complex looking chords. In Grade 4 we're concentrating on root position chords only. For example:

can become

This chord consists of notes from the tonic triad

In a tonic chord, the notes of the triad can be used multiple times in any order, as long as the BOTTOM NOTE IS THE TONIC (scale degree no. 1)!

It is the same for subdominant and dominant chords. Chord IV will have scale degree no. 4 at the bottom and chord V will have scale degree no. 5 at the bottom. The upper notes may be in any order.

You'll be given some music with root position chords and will have to identify chords I, IV and V. This may seem complicated, but all you really need to do is look at the bottom note of the chord to see if it is scale degree 1, 4 or 5!

Let's try this one in A major. The chords to identify are labelled as (1), (2) and (3). (Don't let this numbering put you off — these are not the chord numbers! This is just the way you'll see it in your exam.)

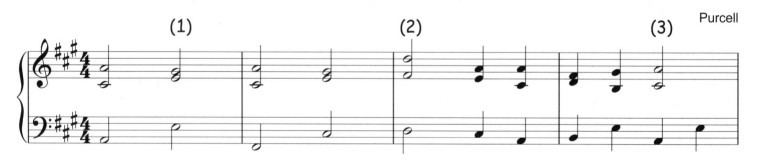

Which scale degree is the bass note at (1) ? ___ So this is chord ___

Which scale degree is the bass note at (2) ? ___ So this is chord ___

Which scale degree is the bass note at (3) ? ___ So this is chord ___

 REMEMBER... In Grade 4, all of the chords are in root position. So even though the notes are spread out over 2 (or more!) staves, you only need to look at the lowest note. Pretty conveninent, don't you think?

Here are some more examples. Identify the numbered chords with Roman numerals as the tonic (I), subdominant (IV) or dominant (V).

Key: E♭ major

Chord (1): _____

Chord (2): _____

Chord (3): _____

Key: G major

Chord (1): _____

Chord (2): _____

Chord (3): _____

Key: B♭ major

Chord (1): _____

Chord (2): _____

Chord (3): _____

# Rather Important Test

1. Study this section of a piece by Bartók and answer the questions below.    /10

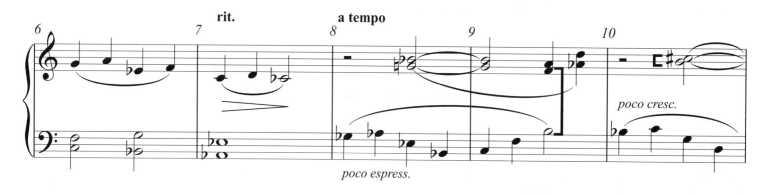

a) Explain the following terms:

   *poco espress.* _____

   **rit**. _____

   **a tempo** _____

b) What is the name of the sign on the bass chord in bar 2? _____

c) How many perfect 5ths are there in the left-hand (bass) part? ____

d) What is the meaning of the time signature? _____

e) What is another way of writing this time signature?

f) Name the intervals (by number and type) marked with vertical brackets:

   Bar 4: _____    Bar 9: _____    Bar 10: _____

2. Here is a short excerpt by Wagner. Insert the correct time signature and draw a bracket over seven consective notes that form a chromatic scale.    /2

3. Write a complete four-bar rhythm in $\frac{6}{8}$ time using the given opening. /10
   (Remember to complete the first bar, and be careful with your last bar!)

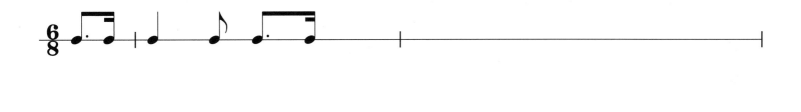

4. Insert the correct time signature for this excerpt, and identify the chords /4
   marked with an asterisk. (Hint: the last chord is done for you)

5. This maths question relates to the left hand (bass) part of the example above: /3

   (Value of rest bar 1) + (Value of first note bar 4) x (Number of books in Harry
   Potter series) = _____

6. Write these triads using accidentals instead of a key signature. /6

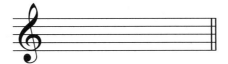
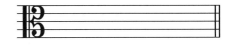

E major, V                         D♭ major, I                         F minor, IV

   Total:   /35

# Setting Words to Rhythm

The first thing you should do when setting words to a rhythm is mark the accented words or syllables in the poetry you are given. Do this by drawing an upright line **just before** each important syllable, which can sometimes be in the middle of a word, for example:

|Jack be|nimble, |Jack be|quick

|Jack jump|over the |candle|stick

If we treat these upright lines as bar lines, we can see which are the strong beats of each 'bar', as well as how many syllables are in each.

The number of syllables in each bar (between each upright line) will determine which rhythmic pattern you use:

| | 1 syllable per bar e.g. 'quick' | 2 syllables per bar e.g. 'Jack be' | 3 syllables per bar e.g. 'o-ver the' |
|---|---|---|---|
| $\frac{2}{4}$ | 𝅗𝅥 | ♩ ♩ | ♩♫ or ♫♩ |
| $\frac{3}{4}$ | 𝅗𝅥. | 𝅗𝅥 ♩ | ♩ ♩ ♩ |
| $\frac{3}{8}$ | ♩. | ♩ ♪ | ♫♪ |

So if we were to write a rhythm in $\frac{3}{4}$ to the verse above, it would look like this:

Jack    be    nim - ble Jack    be    quick,    Jack    jump    o - ver the    can - dle - stick.

Notice how the syllables are spaced exactly under the notes, and words with more than one syllable are 'hyphenated' (which means there is a hyphen (—) separating the syllables).

The table above deals with $\frac{2}{4}$, $\frac{3}{4}$, and $\frac{3}{8}$ as there is **one** strong beat per bar in these time signatures. Now let's explore other time signatures...

In the time signatures of $\frac{4}{4}$ and $\frac{6}{8}$, there is one strong AND one medium accent in each bar. The upright lines show us where the strong and medium accents are, which means each upright line represents **half** a bar, not a whole bar.

When inventing rhythms in $\frac{4}{4}$ and $\frac{6}{8}$, use the following rhythmic patterns:

| | 1 syllable per **half** bar e.g. 'stick' | 2 syllables per **half** bar e.g. 'can-dle' | 3 syllables per **half** bar e.g. 'o-ver the' |
|---|---|---|---|
| $\frac{4}{4}$ or **C** | | | |
| $\frac{6}{8}$ | | | |

Here is 'Jack be nimble' again, this time in $\frac{6}{8}$: (Notice how this time there are only four bars instead of eight!)

Jack   be nim - ble   Jack   be quick,   Jack   jump o - ver the   can - dle - stick.

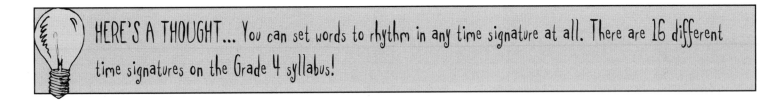

HERE'S A THOUGHT... You can set words to rhythm in any time signature at all. There are 16 different time signatures on the Grade 4 syllabus!

Now you have a go. Set the verse 'Jack be nimble' to a rhythm, using the time signature of $\frac{2}{4}$, $\frac{3}{8}$ or **C**. Write the words correctly underneath the notes, separating each syllable with a hyphen. If your rhythm goes onto a second line, don't write the time signature again - it should only appear once! (Also, try to keep four bars to a line.)

Rhythm: _____

Words: ........................................................................

_____

........................................................................

# The Anacrusis in Poetry

Sometimes the first word or syllable of a line is not accented. All you have to do is remember that the upright lines show us the accented words in each bar.

The | wind was | strong, the | rain was | harsh,

The | storm was the | worst of the | year so | far.

In the first line, 'The' will be an anacrusis.

In the second line, 'The' is not accented and actually belongs in the bar before. It will go in the same bar as 'harsh'.

It's best to use a crotchet anacrusis in $\frac{2}{4}$, $\frac{3}{4}$, $\frac{4}{4}$ and $\mathbf{C}$, and a quaver anacrusis in $\frac{3}{8}$ and $\frac{6}{8}$. But here's the most important thing to remember...

### YOU MUST ADJUST YOUR FINAL BAR!

See if you can finish these rhythms to the verse above. (Refer to the rhythmic patterns on pages 48 and 49.) Remember to deduct the value of the anacrusis from the last bar!

The    wind   was ......................................................................................................

The    wind   was ......................................................................................................

REMEMBER: Write the time signature on the first line only, even if your rhythm takes up two lines!

50

# More About Rhythm Writing

Sometimes the second line of poetry is a little shorter, and you may end up with only seven accents, like this:

I |used to like |winter but |now I like |spring

The |flowers are |ev'ry|where.

In time signatures like $\frac{2}{4}$, $\frac{3}{4}$ and $\frac{3}{8}$, it is **not enough** to have only seven bars – this is not regarded as a 'balanced' rhythm. You must add an 8th bar and tie the last note over, e.g.

Look! The eighth bar allows for the anacrusis

Try writing this verse again in $\frac{2}{4}$:

Rhythm: _____

Words: ...................................................................................................

_____

...................................................................................................

## Top Tips for Writing Rhythms

❧ Mark the accents first

❧ In $\frac{2}{4}$, $\frac{3}{4}$ and $\frac{3}{8}$, each accent represents one bar

❧ In $\frac{4}{4}$ and $\frac{6}{8}$, each accent represents HALF a bar

❧ If you have only seven bars, remember to add an eighth bar and tie the last note over

❧ If there is an anacrusis, make sure you adjust the last bar

Write balanced rhythms to the following couplets. Write the words clearly under the notes, and hyphenate words with more than one syllable. Choose a different time signature for each couplet!

Tomorrow I'm going to wash the car
My Dad will be very pleased!

Rhythm: _____

Words: .........................................................................

_____

.........................................................................

Traffic lights, traffic lights red and green,
Then there's amber in between.

Rhythm: _____

Words: .........................................................................

_____

.........................................................................

They all say it is easy to swim
But no-one can do it as fast as Jim.

Rhythm: _____

Words: .........................................................................

_____

.........................................................................

Go to www.blitzbooks.com for more practice in rhythm writing!

52

# Adding Variety

Check out this setting of words to rhythm:

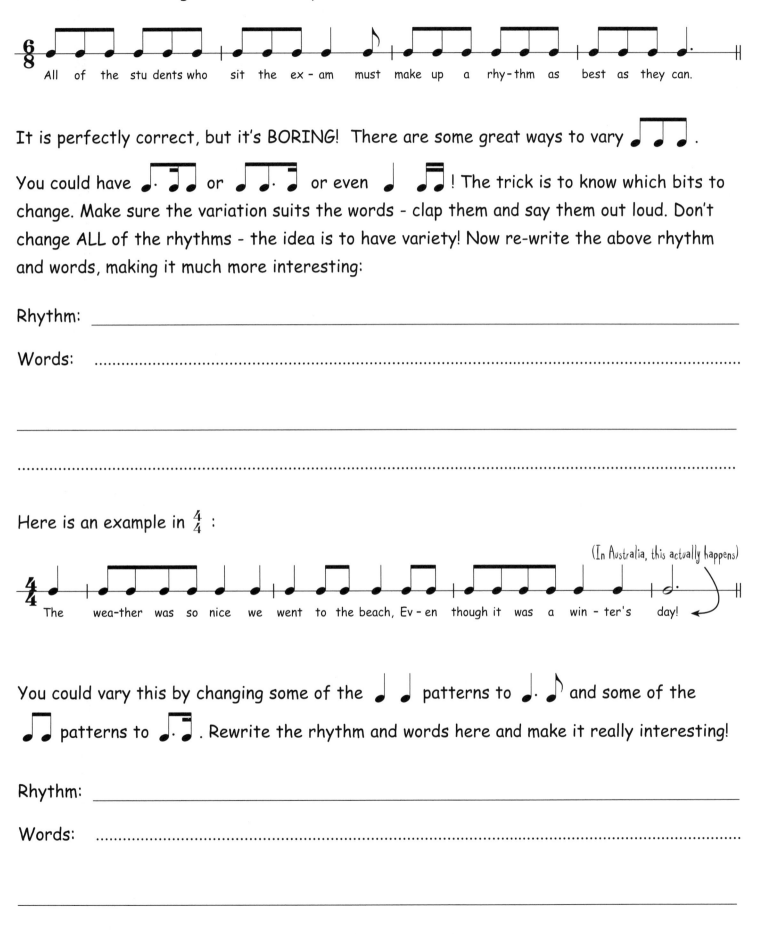

It is perfectly correct, but it's BORING! There are some great ways to vary ♩♪♪.

You could have ♩.♪♪ or ♪♪♩. or even ♩ ♪♪ ! The trick is to know which bits to change. Make sure the variation suits the words - clap them and say them out loud. Don't change ALL of the rhythms - the idea is to have variety! Now re-write the above rhythm and words, making it much more interesting:

Rhythm: _____

Words: .................................................................................

_____

.................................................................................

Here is an example in $\frac{4}{4}$ :

You could vary this by changing some of the ♩ ♩ patterns to ♩. ♪ and some of the ♪♪ patterns to ♩.♪. Rewrite the rhythm and words here and make it really interesting!

Rhythm: _____

Words: .................................................................................

_____

.................................................................................

# Stretching Syllables (Or: Adding Even More Interest)

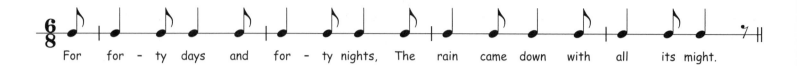

Sometimes a rhythm can be a little boring, but in a way that is hard to fix, e.g.

For for - ty days and for - ty nights, The rain came down with all its might.

The best way to vary this rhythm is to **add** some notes! But to do this correctly you must remember this rule:

### If two or more notes share one syllable, the notes **MUST** have a slur!
(It would be better not to add the notes than to forget the slur!)

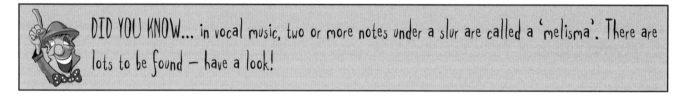

Pick some interesting syllables in the rhythm above and add some quavers - with slurs!

DID YOU KNOW... in vocal music, two or more notes under a slur are called a 'melisma'. There are lots to be found — have a look!

Make these rhythms more interesting by adding some notes. (Don't forget the slurs!)

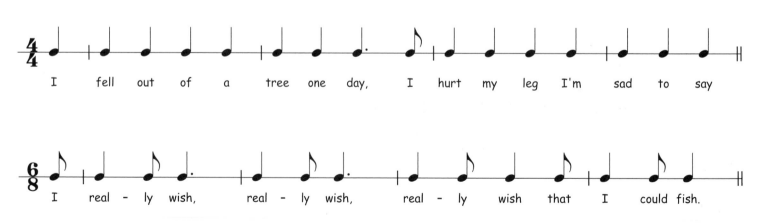

I fell out of a tree one day, I hurt my leg I'm sad to say

I real - ly wish, real - ly wish, real - ly wish that I could fish.

Go to **www.blitzbooks.com** and download the 'Creative Couplets' page. Compose some really INTERESTING rhythms, using different time signatures and using extra notes and slurs!

# Incredibly Short Quiz

1. Write a rhythm to this couplet, writing the words clearly under the notes.

> The chorus frogs in the big lagoon
>
> Would sing their songs to the silvery moon

Henry Lawson

Rhythm: _____

Words: ........................................................................................

_____

........................................................................................

2. Write a one-octave descending chromatic scale beginning on this note.

3. Identify the chords (I, IV or V) marked with an asterisk in this excerpt by Rossini, and then answer the maths questions below.

a) How many bars feature double dots? _____

b) How many demisemiquavers is the rest in bar 1 equal to? _____

# Orchestral Instruments

In your exam you're expected to know a few facts about the most common orchestral instruments. The tables below are designed to help, but there is LOADS of information on the internet about this. It's a great idea to read widely about the way the sound is produced and what material each instrument is usually made of.

Here are four tables, each featuring a different section of the orchestra. **The instruments in each section are listed from the highest sounding to the lowest sounding.**

## STRINGS

| Instrument (highest to lowest) | Usual clef | Common terms and signs | Interesting facts about strings |
|---|---|---|---|
| Violin | 𝄞 | *con sordino*: play with mute<br>*sul ponticello*: play on or near the bridge<br><br>⋁  up bow<br><br>⊓  down bow<br><br>*arco*: with the bow<br><br>*pizzicato*: pluck the strings<br><br>*sul G*: play on the G string | The bow is drawn across the strings to make them vibrate and produce sound<br><br>Double bass music is written an octave higher than it sounds<br><br>The full name for cello is actually 'violoncello' |
| Viola | 𝄡 | | |
| Cello | 𝄢 | | |
| Double bass | 𝄢 | | |

## WOODWIND

| Instrument (highest to lowest) | Usual clef | Common terms and signs | Interesting facts about woodwinds |
|---|---|---|---|
| Piccolo | 𝄞 | Flutter tonguing<br><br>, <br>(breath mark) | Air is blown across or into the mouthpiece to make the column of air vibrate<br><br>The piccolo sounds an octave higher than written<br><br>Flute and piccolo are the only non-reed instruments<br><br>The saxophone is a woodwind instrument but is not usually in an orchestra |
| Flute | 𝄞 | | |
| Oboe | 𝄞 | | |
| Clarinet | 𝄞 | | |
| Bassoon | 𝄢 | | |

# BRASS

| Instrument (highest to lowest) | Usual clef | Common terms and signs | Interesting facts about brass |
|---|---|---|---|
| Trumpet | 𝄞 | *con sordino*: play with mute | Brass and strings are the only sections that use mutes |
| Horn | 𝄞 | *fp (forte-piano)*: loud then immediately soft | The horn is the only brass instrument included in a wind quintet (with the four woodwinds listed opposite) |
| Trombone | 𝄢 | | |
| Tuba | 𝄢 | | The tuba is also known as the bass tuba |

# PERCUSSION

| Instrument (highest to lowest) | Usual clef | Common terms and signs | Interesting facts about percussion |
|---|---|---|---|
| Timpani | 𝄢 | Roll (like a trill) | Many percussion instruments are struck with sticks or mallets (or against each other, as with cymbals) |
| Side drum | n/a | ✗ (unpitched notehead) | |
| Bass drum | n/a | | Other pitched percussion instruments commonly found in the orchestra are xylophone, marimba and glockenspiel |
| Triangle | n/a | | |

There are quite a few orchestral instruments not listed on this page! See if you can research some facts about four other instruments, and list them in this table:

| Instrument (highest to lowest) | Usual clef | Orchestral family | Common terms and signs | Interesting fact |
|---|---|---|---|---|
| | | | | |
| | | | | |
| | | | | |
| | | | | |

# Instruments and Other Things

The following extract is from a Mozart string quartet. Insert the correct clefs!

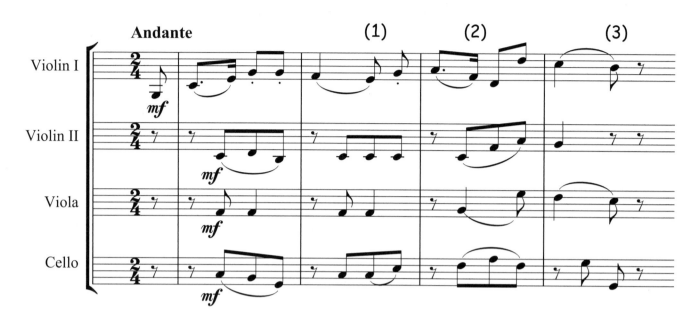

Now name each numbered chord above. Remember you are looking at all four parts.

Key: **C major**    Chord (1): _____

Chord (2): _____

Chord (3): _____

The next piece is written for a solo instrument with piano accompaniment. Name three instruments that could play the top part: _____

Purcell

Name the key of the extract above: _____.

# Ornaments

In Grade 4 you have to know about the standard ornaments used in music. You have most likely come across a few of these in the pieces you've played!

| Ornament | Name | Description | Actual Sound |
|---|---|---|---|
| ♩ | Upper mordent | Quick alternation with the note above | |
| ♩ | Lower mordent | Quick alternation with the note below | |
| tr ♩ | Trill (or shake) | Rapid continuous alternation with the note above (or another specified note) | |
| ♩ | Acciaccatura (or 'crushed note') | Fast note/s played with or just before the main note | |
| ♩ | Appoggiatura* (or 'leaning note') | Occurs on the beat and usually takes half or two-thirds of the value of the main note | |
| ♩ | Turn | A rapid four-note motif: note above/main note/note below/main note | |

*The appoggiatura is the only ornament that has any rhythmic value of its own.

In your exam you will have to identify and name any of the ornaments listed above. Try it with this piece of music (N.B. the very last one is not an ornament!):

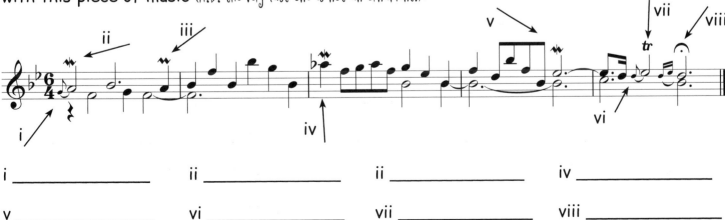

i _____  ii _____  ii _____  iv _____

v _____  vi _____  vii _____  viii _____

# Ornaments and Stuff

There are four ornaments in the following extract from a piece by C.P.E. Bach. Can you find and name them? (Hint: three of them are on a single note!!)

1. _____  2. _____  3. _____  4. _____

Just for fun, find out the rhythm name of the last two notes in bar two (it has eight syllables!):

_____

Study the music below by d'Anglebert. How many lower mordents are there? _____ How many upper mordents? _____ Now insert the time signature and missing bar-lines.

Here is one more excerpt, by Gluck. Answer the questions below.

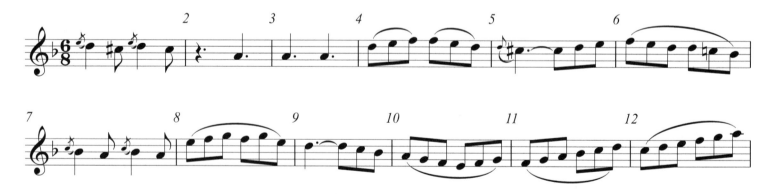

What's the difference between the ornaments in bar 1 and the ornament in bar 5?

_____

If the ornament in bar 5 lasts for two quavers, how long does the C♯ last? _____

Name two keys that share this key signature: _____ and _____

60

# Terms

←——————→

Notice how this page is not called '**Italian** Terms'? That's because there are some FRENCH terms to learn in Grade 4 as well as Italian! (Lucky you) Remember, you need to know these **in addition to** all the terms you learned in Grades 1–3. Find them all at **www.blitzbooks.com**

## Italian

| | | |
|---|---|---|
| *affettuoso* | - | tenderly |
| *affrettando* | - | hurrying |
| *amabile* | - | amiable, pleasant |
| *appassionato* | - | passionately |
| *calando* | - | getting softer and slower |
| *cantando* | - | in a singing style |
| *come* | - | like, similar to |
| *facile* | - | easy |
| *fuoco* | - | fire |
| *giusto* | - | exact (e.g. 'tempo giusto' = exact time) |
| *l'istesso tempo* | - | at the same speed |
| *morendo* | - | dying away |
| *niente* | - | nothing |
| *nobilmente* | - | nobly |
| *perdendosi* | - | dying away, losing sound |
| *presto possibile* | - | as fast as possible |
| *quasi* | - | like, resembling |
| *sonoro* | - | resonant |
| *sopra* | - | above |
| *sotto voce* | - | 'below voice'; in an undertone |
| *veloce* | - | swift |

## French

| | | |
|---|---|---|
| *a* | - | to, at |
| *anime* | - | animated |
| *assez* | - | enough |
| *avec* | - | with |
| *cédez* | - | yield, slow down |
| *douce* | - | sweet |
| *doucement* | - | sweetly |
| *en dehors* | - | bring out the sound |
| *en retenant* | - | hold back the tempo |
| *et* | - | and |
| *légèrement* | - | lightly |
| *lent* | - | slow |
| *mais* | - | but |
| *moins* | - | less |
| *modéré* | - | at a moderate speed |
| *non* | - | not |
| *peu* | - | little |
| *plus* | - | more |
| *presser* | - | hurry, go faster |
| *ralentir* | - | slow down |
| *retenu* | - | held back |
| *sans* | - | without |
| *très* | - | very |
| *un, une* | - | a, one (e.g. 'un peu' = a little) |
| *vif* | - | lively |
| *vite* | - | fast, quick |

# Crossword

## Across

2. Italian for 'swift'
5. Scale consisting entirely of semitones
9. Notes worth two semibreves
11. French word meaning 'very'
12. Hot food encased in pastry (not essential Grade 4 knowledge)
13. Type of interval one semitone smaller than perfect
15. English meaning of 'fuoco'
18. Music for _____ is written in alto clef
19. Name this ornament:
20. Type of interval one semitone larger than major
23. Meaning of French term 'lent'
24. Do _____ page in this workbook to blitz your exam!
25. Highest instrument in a wind quintet
26. Lowest instrument in the brass family
27. $\frac{9}{16}$ is compound_____ time

## Down

1. Clef normally used by the oboe
3. Type of time containing dotted beats
4. Italian term that strings and brass players see when asked to play with mute
6. Brass instrument that features in wind quintets
7. Pitched percussion instrument
8. French term equivalent to 'ritardando'
10. Technical name for scale degree no. 6
14. French word for 'without'
16. General name for signs indicating decorative added notes
17. Person with no magical powers (e.g. in Harry Potter)
19. The leading note is the _____ note of the dominant triad (in root position)
21. Two notes played in the time of three
22. This is pulled across the strings of stringed instruments to make them vibrate
23. Another name for 'trill'

# Use Your Skills

It's time to put all your knowledge to the test. You'll be applying pretty much all of the skills you've learned in this book over the next few pages! Study each excerpt and answer the questions that follow.

C.P.E. Bach

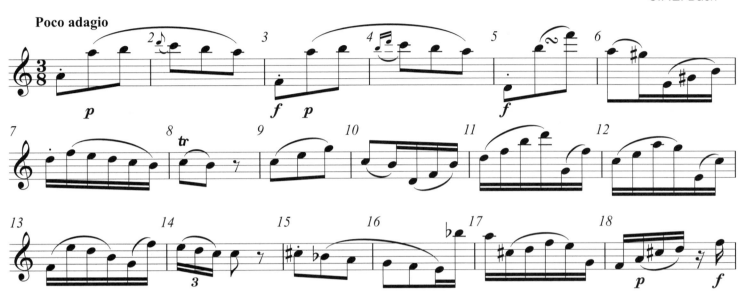

★ The key is ____ minor.

★ What is the letter name of the highest note? _____ And the technical name? _____

★ What is the meaning of the tempo indication? _____

★ How many bars contain ornaments? _____ Name the ornament used in bar 5. _____

★ Rewrite bars 14 and 15 using a compound time signature, keeping the sound the same.

★ True or false: this music was written by J.S. Bach's brother. _____

★ Add an Italian term at bar 9 that means 'to play in an amiable, pleasant style'.

★ Name two differences between bars 1–2 and 3–4. _____

_____

★ Add the time signature.

★ What does *'poco ad lib.'* mean? _____

★ Name the ornament in the last bar. _____

★ Rewrite bar 6 in the alto clef, keeping the pitch the same. Write the key signature.

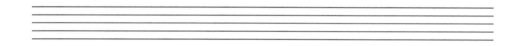

★ How many bars contain triplets? ____ What is the value, in quaver beats, of each of these triplets? ____

★ Write as a breve the enharmonic equivalent of the last note of bar 1.

★ Circle two possible instruments that could play this music:

**timpani**          **violin**          **cello**          **triangle**          **flute**

★ Name two keys that share the key signature of this excerpt: _____

★ True or false: bar 8 contains the only demisemiquavers in the piece.

★ Add a French term in bar 3 that means 'to relax the speed'.

★ Insert the missing time signature.

★ Name the stringed instrument for which this piece is most likely written: _____

★ Name and explain the sign over the semiquaver triplets in bar 1. _____

_____

★ Give the English meaning of the French terms in this extract:

ralentir _____

*vif* _____

*douce* _____

★ Why do you think bar 2 is written in the treble clef? _____

★ Rewrite the bracketed interval in bar 3 in the treble clef, then name the interval.

                              Name: _____

★ Add an Italian tempo marking that means 'to play as fast as possible'.

★ $H_2O$ is commonly known as _____ (not strictly part of the Grade 4 syllabus)

65

★ Underline two possible instruments that could play this music:

**double bass**          **side drum**          **trumpet**          **tuba**          **violin**

★ Insert the correct time signature.

★ What do the signs on each note in bar 6 mean?_____

★ The notes in bar 7 all belong to the key of ____ major.

★ Add the missing rests in bar 9.

★ Assuming the original key is C major, circle all the dominant notes in this passage.

★ Name the ornament in bar 4. _____

★ Ignoring the ornament, rewrite bar 8 an octave lower using the bass clef.

★ Describe the two melodic intervals marked with a bracket and labelled X and Y:

　　　X: _____ (did you see the accidental earlier in the bar???)

　　　Y: _____

★ True or false: theory books should not contain jokes. _____

★ Add a French term to show that this melody should be brought out, i.e. played prominently.

★ Add a sign to show that the melody should be repeated.

# Test Paper... Sort Of

All theory books end with a test paper, but this one is DIFFERENT. It already has the answers in it (mostly wrong answers!) and your job is to be the teacher – you have to **mark** it.

When you've found all the mistakes, go to **www.blitzbooks.com** and download the EXACT SAME PAPER – this time with no answers already in it. See if you can get 100%!

★ ★ ★ ★ ★ ★ ★

**Theory Paper Grade 4**

**Time allowed: 2 hours**

TOTAL MARKS
100

15

**1**     Look at this extract and then answer the questions below.

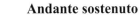

Andante sostenuto

Chopin

a)    Give the meaning of:     (4)

    **Andante sostenuto** ...easy sustained walking......

    *affetuoso* ......sort of like affected......

b)    Draw a bracket over four consecutive notes that form a chromatic scale.     (2)

c)    How many triplets are there in this passage? ....8..........     (2)

d)    Write as a breve the enharmonic equivalent of the last note.     (4)

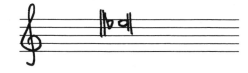

e)    Name and explain the signs under the triplets in bar 6. ...Sideways arrows.........     (3)

**EITHER**

(a)   Write a rhythm on one note, with time signature and bar-lines, to fit the words below.
Write each syllable under the note or notes to which it applies.

As I was going up the stair

I met a man who wasn't there

Anonymous

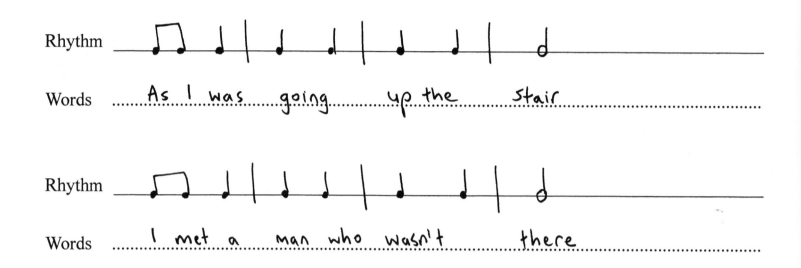

Rhythm

Words .......As....I....was.........going.................up..the..............stair.........................................

Rhythm

Words .........I....met....a.........man....who....wasn't.................there............................................

**OR**

(b) Write a complete four-bar rhythm in $\frac{12}{8}$ time using the given opening.

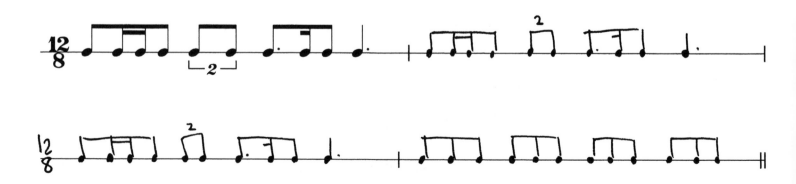

**3**   Study this piece of music and answer the questions below.

Grieg

a)   Insert the correct time signature.   (2)

b)   What does the tempo marking mean? ......In a gusty tempo........................ (1)

c)   This extract begins on the dominant. Name the key: ........D...................... (1)

d)   Name the melodic intervals marked with brackets in bars 11, 12 and 13.

Bar 11 .....dim 4th.          Bar 12 ....min 3rd.....          Bar 13 .....min 7th.... (6)

e)   Rewrite bars 8 and 9 in compound time but without changing the rhythmic effect.   (10)
     Remember to include the new time signature.

f)   The breath marks at the end of bars 9 and 13 indicate that this piece is probably written
     for a woodwind instrument. Name two instruments from this family that could play it.   (2)

     ........flute.............. and ........trumpet..........

g)   Name the ornaments in bars 3 and 4. ...mordent...and...mordent.................... (1)

h)   There are long brackets over the first and last phrases. Mark the other phrases in the   (2)
     same way.

69

i)   Answer True or False to the following statements:

Tubas are the highest-pitched brass instruments.   .....False...........

The term 'con sordino' only applies to strings.   .....True...........

'Arco' is a term you would see after 'pizzicato'.   .....True...........

The timpani is a pitched percussion instrument.   .....True...........

ii)   Name a standard orchestral woodwind instrument that uses the bass clef.

.........~~Cello~~ Bagpipes.........................

4   a)   Write the key signature of B major and then one octave descending
of that scale. Use semibreves.

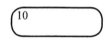

b)   Add all necessary sharp, flat or natural signs in order to make a chromatic scale
beginning on the given note.

5     Rewrite this melody in the alto clef so that it sounds one octave higher.

Fauré

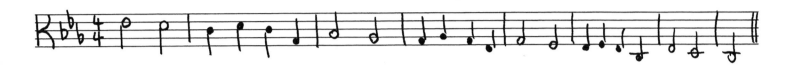

6     Look at this music by Bartók and answer the questions below.

a)     Name and explain three types of articulation used.

......Accent — play louder.......................................................

......Accent with line — play louder and longer.......

......Little wedges — super short.........................................

b)     Insert the correct time signature.

c)     Write the rest that would fill an entire bar in this time signature.

71

**7**    (a)    Name each of the numbered chords as tonic (I), subdominant (IV) or dominant (V). The key is C major.

Chord:

(1)    ....Tonic............................

(2)    ....Subdominant............

(3)    ....Dominant...................

(9)

(b)    Identify these triads by naming the key and describing them as I, IV or V.    (6)

Key:    ....Gᵇ major.......      ....E major.......      ....Bᵇ major......

Triad:    ........II........      ........I........      ........V.II........

 How did you do marking this paper? Did you find lots of mistakes? Now go to www.blitzbooks.com and download the uncompleted version. Good luck!